BBC Children's Books

Published by the Penguin Group

Penguin Books Ltd, 80 Strand, London, WC2R 0RL, England

Penguin Group (USA) Inc., 375 Hudson Street, New York, New York 10014, USA

Penguin Books (Australia) Ltd, 250 Camberwell Road, Camberwell, Victoria 3124, Australia (A division of Pearson Australia Group Pty Ltd)

Canada, India, New Zealand, South Africa

Published by BBC Children's Books, 2009

Text and design © Children's Character Books, 2009

Images © BBC 2004

Pages 20-25 written by Trevor Baxendale

Pages 40-45 written by Christopher Cooper

Pages 8-9, 12-13, 16-7, 28-29. 32-39 and 54-59 written by Jonathan Green

Pages 6-7, 14-15, 26-27, 30-31 and 46-53 written by Moray Laing

Pages 10-11 and 18-19 written by Justin Richards

Illustrations by John Ross

Colours by James Offredi

10 9 8 7 6 5 4 3 2 1

ISBN-13: 978-1-40590-494-0

Printed in Italy

Contents

Who is The Doctor?

The First Doctor

It's hard to imagine the man opposite is the same man as the Tenth Doctor. Bored of his home planet, the First Doctor stole a TARDIS to explore time and space. He could be quite grumpy and unreasonable at times.

The Second Doctor

After a fierce battle with Cybermen, the Doctor suddenly changed into a younger, dark-haired man. This mischievous Doctor called himself a genius and liked to have fun.

The Doctor is a brilliant, amazing man — a Time Lord who is over 900 years old — and we don't even know his proper name. He calls himself the Doctor, but Doctor who exactly?

He comes from a planet called Gallifrey, but his home world is now gone, destroyed in the Last Great Time War during a terrible battle between his people and the Daleks.

Travelling through time and space in an old blue police box — the TARDIS — is an exciting and dangerous life. Along the way he has made many friends, fought hideous creatures, and become more involved than Time Lords should ever admit to.

Most surprising of all, if the Doctor's body is damaged or becomes too old he is able to change, and this process is known as regeneration. The Doctor is currently in his tenth body — but things are about to change again...

POLICE PUBLIC CALL BOX POLICE

POLICE TELEPHONE
FREE
FOR USE OF
PUBLIC
ADVICE & ASSISTANCE
OBTAINABLE IMMEDIATELY
OFFICER & CARS
RESPOND TO ALL CALLS
PULL TO OPEN

Did you know?

Time Lords have two hearts.

Gallifrey is in the constellation of Kasterborous.

The Doctor is the last of the Time Lords.

The Third Doctor

The Time Lords forced the Doctor to change his appearance and sent him to Earth to punish him for stealing the TARDIS and breaking the laws of time. While on Earth, the Third Doctor became UNIT's scientific advisor.

The Fifth Doctor

After falling from a great height, the Doctor regenerated into a much younger body. He chose to wear Edwardian cricket gear and stuck a piece of celery on his jacket.

The Fourth Doctor

When his body was damaged by radiation, he once again regenerated. He wore a long scarf and was very different from the three Doctors before him. Forgiven by the Time Lords, he was now able to explore time and space again.

The Sixth Doctor

The Doctor regenerated after coming into contact with a deadly poison. This Doctor had very bad taste and wore awful clothes! He was a much bossier and louder character than before.

The Seventh Doctor

Travelling in the TARDIS is fun, but can be dangerous! When the TARDIS was shot down by the Rani, the Doctor was injured and forced to regenerate. This time, he turned into an energetic and mysterious man.

The Eighth Doctor

Landing back on Earth, the Doctor was attacked and regenerated after an incident on a hospital operating table. This Doctor wore slightly eccentric clothes, not unlike the First Doctor.

The Ninth Doctor

We're not sure what brought on this regeneration — but it's likely to be connected to the Time War, which the Ninth Doctor blamed himself for not being able to stop it. This Doctor's body died when he absorbed the Time Vortex to save Rose.

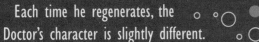

Each time he regenerates, the Doctor's character is slightly different.

The Children of Time...
Where Are They Now?

The Children of Time are mostly former companions of the Doctor, who joined the Last of the Time Lords to battle the Daleks and save the whole of existence. Davros, the Daleks' creator, planned to detonate the Reality Bomb, a device powered by an arrangement of 27 planets, which would have ultimately destroyed reality itself.

After they helped avert the end of everything, they joined the Doctor in piloting the TARDIS as it towed Earth back to our solar system, but what happened to them after that?

Captain Jack, Martha and Mickey

During the Stolen Earth incident, Captain Jack Harkness was able to reactivate the teleport function of his Vortex Manipulator. Locking onto the location of the TARDIS, he arrived in London in time to see the Doctor hit by a Dalek death ray. On-board the Crucible, the Daleks' flagship, he was exterminated and almost incinerated, but Jack's inability to die saved him once again.

When UNIT HQ in New York came under attack from the Daleks, Martha Jones teleported herself to safety, using salvaged Sontaran technology. She was ordered to find the Doctor. If she couldn't manage that she was to trigger the Osterhagen Key, which would detonate twenty-five nuclear warheads, placed at strategic locations beneath Earth's crust, thereby destroying the planet. However, she, too, was captured by the Daleks. On-board the Crucible, she helped engineer their defeat.

Martha Jones is now back with what remains of UNIT and looking forward to married life.

Captain Jack Harkness is back at the Torchwood Hub in Cardiff with Ianto Jones and Gwen Cooper, monitoring activity from the space-time rift that lies beneath the Welsh capital...

Mickey Smith decided there was nothing left for him on the parallel Earth, and so chose to stay in our world. But what will become of him now?

Rose Tyler

When Rose first met the Doctor, she could never have guessed how it would change her. Trapped on a parallel Earth, when reality faced destruction at the hands of a New Dalek Empire, she crossed into our Universe to find the Doctor and stand by his side in the battle.

With the Dalek race apparently wiped out by the Duplicate Doctor, the Last of the Time Lords realised that his other, part-human self was too dangerous to be left on his own and that the only person who could make him a better person was Rose. The Doctor took Rose and his duplicate to Bad Wolf Bay in Norway on the parallel Earth, before the universes were sealed off from one another once again.

Sarah Jane Smith

A former travelling companion of the Doctor's and now a freelance investigative journalist, Sarah Jane Smith met the Doctor again, in his tenth incarnation, when the two of them were investigating reported alien activity at Deffry Vale High School.

When the Daleks stole Earth, she set off to find him again. She was taken on to the Daleks' flagship, along with Mickey Smith and Jackie Tyler, who had made the dimension jump from the parallel Earth to help Rose. Sarah Jane gave Captain Jack the Warp Star with which he threatened to destroy the Crucible.

Sarah Jane is now back at 13 Bannerman Road, with her adopted son Luke, K-9 the super-intelligent robot dog, and the alien Xylok computer Mr Smith.

Donna Noble

A temp from Chiswick when they first met, Donna's travels with the Doctor changed her. When she became the DoctorDonna — with a Time Lord brain in a human body — for one moment she was the most important woman in the Universe. Grateful species sang her praises from one end of the cosmos to the other.

But she can never know how important she was to the fate of the Universe. Donna's mind could not cope with the knowledge it gained when she became the DoctorDonna, and it was killing her. To save her life, the Doctor had to wipe her memory, removing all traces of him and their adventures. Now living with her Mum Sylvia and Granddad Wilf, she no longer has any memory of her experiences with the Doctor and the TARDIS, but that didn't stop her being, as the Doctor would put it, 'Brilliant!'

The Next Doctor

The Doctor's been travelling on his own since the defeat of Davros and the Daleks. So he is surprised to hear someone calling his name. Except, when he goes to help it isn't him they want. It's another Doctor! It's London, Christmas 1851, when the Doctor meets another man who claims to be the Doctor — the one and only. The real Doctor doesn't have time to solve this mystery though, because they are confronted by a creature that seems to be part animal, part Cyberman — a CyberShade. The Doctors try to capture it, but it's too strong. They manage to escape, with the help of the other Doctor's companion Rosita. The real Doctor is beginning to think that things are not what they seem. The other Doctor's sonic screwdriver is just a screwdriver, and his TARDIS turns out to be a hot air balloon. What's more, he can't remember anything before he encountered the Cybermen... The Cybermen themselves certainly think that the 'other' Doctor is the real Doctor. They're working with a lady called Miss Hartigan and people who can provide them with children as slave labour. The Cybermen are building something, something huge...

Trying to find out what the Cybermen are up to, the two Doctors investigate the disappearance of a man called Jackson Lake. At his house, they find Cyber technology — info-stamps that contain vast amounts of computer data that the Cybermen can download into themselves. And one of the info-stamps is all about the Doctor!

Cybermen attack, and the Doctor tries to fight them off with a sword! But it's the other Doctor who saves the day — using the info-stamp as a weapon to destroy the Cybermen by blasting data at them...

The Doctor realises this has happened before. Jackson Lake saved himself by using an infostamp — the info-stamp about the Doctor. And the data streamed out of it into his mind. The other Doctor is really Jackson Lake, his mind full of the real Doctor's history and background...

Meanwhile, the Cybermen's plan is moving ahead. They have built a CyberKing — a Dreadnought Class Spaceship that rises up to tower over London. It's a factory too, ready to turn millions of people into new Cybermen. To her surprise and against her will, Miss Hartigan is wired into the systems — she becomes the mind of the CyberKing...

With the help of Rosita and Jackson Lake, the Doctor manages to free the enslaved children — including Lake's own son. But he still has to stop the CyberKing. And for that he needs the TARDIS — the other Doctor's TARDIS. The hot air balloon.

The Doctor gets close enough in the balloon to pour info-stamp energy into Miss Hartigan. But he isn't trying to kill her — he's set her free, liberating her from the Cyber systems. Horrified at what she has become, her mind rebels. She destroys the Cybermen and the CyberKing is sent back into the Void.

Jackson Lake is reunited with his son, but his wife was killed by the Cybermen. He invites the Doctor to join them for Christmas lunch.

The Doctor politely turns down the offer. Though he has something to show the man who came so close to being the Doctor.

The real TARDIS.

But Jackson Lake perhaps knows the Doctor better than anyone else. He has been the Doctor. He knows how he has suffered as his companions move on and leave him... So, finally, Jackson Lake persuades the Doctor to come to Christmas dinner after all.

Secrets of The Daleks!

The Doctor has battled the Daleks more times than he cares to remember. But just when it looks like they've been defeated at last, the Daleks always somehow manage to return, with renewed plans of conquest. Perhaps the answer to defeating the Daleks is knowledge, but how much do you know about the Doctor's greatest enemy?

Across

7 The extraterrestrial metal from which Dalek armour is made. (10)

9 Created by Dalek genetic experiments that merged humans with animals. (3,6)

12 The clash between the Cybermen and Daleks centred upon Torchwood Tower (3,6,2,6,5)

14 Dalek measurement of time. (4)

15 Geocomtex's secret underground base, beneath the Utah desert, in which a Dalek was imprisoned. (3,5)

16 Four Daleks escaped the defeat of the Emperor Dalek's new Dalek army on board this craft. (4,4)

18 Gallifreyan prison in which the Time Lords had trapped millions of Daleks (7,3)

19 A weapon, developed by the Daleks, capable of destroying all matter, in every universe. (7,4)

20 The leader of the Daleks that stole planet Earth. (7,5)

Down

1 This Dalek travelled into the past, into the Time War, and went mad. (4)

2 The Dalek flagship hidden within the Medusa Cascade along with 27 stolen planets. (3,8)

3 Legendary battle fought between the Daleks and the Time Lords. (4,3)

4 The Daleks intended to use this famous New York landmark as a gamma radiation conductor. (6,5,8)

5 The Dalek Emperor used this huge space station to manipulate the development of mankind in the future. (9,4)

6 The Daleks' home planet. (5)

8 Rose Tyler absorbed its power to erase the Emperor Dalek's army from existence. (4,6)

10 The American internet billionaire who kept a Dalek in chains as part of his private collection of extraterrestrial artefacts. (5,3,7)

11 Dalek Sec merged with this man to become the first Dalek-Human hybrid. (2,8

13 Legendary group of four Daleks with individual personalities. (4,2,5)

17 The megalomaniacal scientist who created the Daleks in his own image. (6)

Davros Detected!

Davros is trying to escape the destruction of the Crucible. He must be stopped! But which one is the real Davros? Can you spot ten differences between the genuine creator of the Daleks and his clone copy?

5 best adventures

New life

Rose discovered the Doctor was alien when she ran into his TARDIS to escape an Auton. When she later saved the Doctor's life, he offered her the chance to travel with him. She couldn't say no, could she?

Father's Day

Rose's dad Pete died when she was very young, so she asked the Doctor if they could use the TARDIS to go back in time to see him before he died. Unable to stop herself, Rose saved him — and created a dangerous wound in time.

The Doctor and... Rose

After she met the Doctor, Rose Tyler's life was never the same again. They ran into each other when he was trying to stop the Autons from destroying Earth and they immediately became the best of friends.

Fast Facts

- In the parallel Earth, Jackie and Pete had a dog called Rose, but no daughter!

- When Rose went off in the TARDIS she was listed as missing and her mum didn't see her for a year.

- She now lives on a parallel Earth with a human version of the Doctor.

Trapped

At the end of a battle with the Daleks and the Cybermen, Rose risked her life to rid the world of the monsters. She was rescued by her parallel dad but became trapped in an alternative world without the Doctor.

Dalek destroyer

She broke into the heart of the TARDIS and absorbed the space time vortex so that she could save the Doctor. This power allowed her to destroy the Daleks, but her actions caused the Doctor to regenerate.

Finding the Doctor

After a long search, Rose broke through into our world and met the Doctor again when the Daleks stole Earth. She helped him, along with several of his other friends to destroy the Daleks. But he eventually returned her to the parallel Earth...

Earth Invaders

Earth is a blue-green gem of a planet perfect for supporting life in all its myriad forms. This suitability for sustaining life has made it the target of many an alien invasion. But have no fear, the Doctor hasn't been far behind, ready to save his adopted home world time, after time, after time...

AD 79 – The Pyroviles

Thousands of years ago, fleeing the loss of their home world, the Pyroviles crashed on Earth. There they remained, their bodies fragmented and dormant, until tremors from volcanic Mount Vesuvius reawakened them.

Aided by the Sibylline Sisterhood of Pompeii and the Cult of Vulcan, they planned to transform the human race into Pyroviles and establish a new Pyrovillian empire on the planet.

1599 – The Carrionites

The Carrionites were wraithlike, skeletal aliens from Rexel 4 in the Rexel Planetary Configuration. The species had been cast out into the Deep Darkness by the Eternals when the Universe was still young but three escaped to 16th century England.

They planned to use the words of Shakespeare to release the rest of their race from their prison and initiate a Millennium of Blood on Earth.

1851 – Cybermen

Cybermen from a parallel Earth landed in London during the Victorian era. There they allied themselves with Miss Mercy Hartigan and put an army of children to work preparing for the rise of the CyberKing.

The CyberKing was a Dreadnought Class Battleship capable of converting millions and leading an invasion that would see not only the British Empire fall before it, but the whole world.

1930s – The Cult of Skaro

To escape from being sucked into the Void at the climax of the Battle of Canary Wharf, the Cult of Skaro made an emergency temporal shift to 1930s Manhattan.

There they set to work on the Final Experiment, hoping to evolve Dalek-kind by merging Daleks with humans, and from there, take over the world.

2006 — Sycorax

These warrior-scavengers arrived in Earth orbit on Christmas Day 2006 aboard their converted-asteroid starship.

They then proceeded to exert blood control over one third of Earth's population, and demand the surrender of the planet.

2007 — The Battle of Canary Wharf

2007 saw a simultaneous invasion attempt by both the Cybermen of the parallel Earth and the Daleks. Having fled the destruction of the Dalek Empire in the year 200,100 in a Voidship, the Cult of Skaro opened the Genesis Ark, unleashing millions of imprisoned Daleks on the world. The two opposing forces clashed, with London caught in the crossfire.

2007 — Krillitanes

A race of carnivorous aliens who could adapt themselves, by absorbing the physical traits and abilities of the races they conquered. Winged creatures at the time, they sought to solve the Skasas Paradigm, and thereby become gods, by turning the children of Deffry Vale High School into a living supercomputer.

2008-2009 — Toclafane

The assault troops of Prime Minister Harold Saxon (a.k.a. the Master), the Toclafane were what mankind had become at the very end of the Universe 100 trillion years in the future. These last humans had conducted experiments on themselves, dispensing with bodies, retaining only their heads, now installed within technologically advanced metal spheres. They were able to travel back through time to the start of the 21st century and decimate their ancestors — killing more than 600 million people — thanks to the Master's creation of the Paradox Machine, and were instrumental in the foundation of a New Time Lord Empire on Earth.

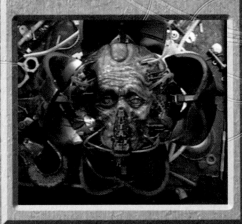

2009 — Sontarans

Clone-bred in batches of millions per hatching, the Sontarans are the finest soldiers in the galaxy. Utterly dedicated to a lifetime of warfare, they must always face their foe in battle and have no fear of death. They have conquered or destroyed thousands of worlds across the galaxy in their ongoing millennia-long war with their mortal enemies the Rutans.

They decided that Earth would make a perfect clone world and set about converting its atmosphere with that very end in mind.

2009 — New Dalek Empire

Originally from the planet Skaro, the Daleks were a mutant life-form, genetically-engineered by the Kaled scientist Davros. Housed within tank-like life-support machines, they were emotionless, impulsive killers, whose primary order was simply to conquer and destroy all other life in the Universe, ensuring the survival and purity of the Dalek race.

Having been rescued from the Time War by Dalek Caan, Davros set about engineering a new race of Daleks from the remains of his own wasted body. This new Dalek Empire prepared to wipe out all of existence with a Reality Bomb powered by an array of twenty-seven planets.

Planet of the Dead

Lady Christina de Souza is a thief. She doesn't need the money, but she loves the challenge and the excitement.

When she steals the ancient gold Cup of Athelstan, she gets more excitement than she bargained for. Escaping from the police on a bus, she ends up sitting right next to the Doctor — as the bus goes through a wormhole and arrives in the scorching desert of a planet with three suns — San Helios.

San Helios was a thriving planet with a population of a hundred billion — until the 'Stingrays' came. They don't have a real name, but they look like huge metal stingrays, flying in a massive swarm round the planet. Flying so fast they create wormholes to other planets — their next feeding grounds.

The creatures eat anything. They can strip a planet bare, like a plague of locusts only much bigger and much deadlier. They have devastated San Helios, reducing the cities and buildings, even the people, to the sand of the desert. It's now a planet of the dead...

The only way back is through the wormhole, and the Doctor and Christina and their friends on the bus have to get back to Earth before the Stingrays. UNIT are ready and waiting on the other side, but there's no way they can fight off a swarm of billions of Stingrays. So it's up to the Doctor and Christina, with help over the phone from UNIT technical genius Malcolm Taylor, to get the bus back through the wormhole then close it up.

Only the bus is bogged down in the sand. And it's run out of fuel. And it weighs tonnes.

Christina might think that things can't get any worse — even if she gets back through the wormhole, she knows the police are waiting to arrest her. But then she meets a Tritovore — a six foot tall alien fly, and he's holding a gun.

There are two Tritovores — Sorvin and Praygat. They're actually quite friendly, though Christina can't understand their weird chirping speech. Luckily, the Doctor can — and the Tritovores can understand him. Their ship crashed on San Helios too. They're just as trapped as the people on the bus.

Carmen's Warning

Carmen and her husband Lou are two of the other people trapped on the bus. Carmen is mildly psychic – every week she wins £10 on the lottery. Passing through the wormhole has strengthened her abilities, and she can sense the approaching stingray swarm. She can hear the dead of San Helios crying out to her...

Once they are back on Earth and safe, she has a warning for the Doctor – 'Your song is ending... It is returning through the dark... He will knock four times.'

The Doctor doesn't know what she means. Not yet.

But he is going to find out...

And they've got fuel – a Crystal Nucleus system the Doctor knows he can adapt to get the bus moving again. The only trouble is, it's a long way down an access shaft.

Luckily, Christina's got her equipment with her – and before the Doctor can talk her out of it, she's diving down the shaft on a wire. She manages to deactivate the security beams that would cut her to pieces, and she gets the Crystal! She also discovers why the ship crashed – it flew into the Stingrays. Now there are Stingrays on the ship, trapped in the engines.

Christina manages to get out of the shaft with the Crystal, but the Stingrays are attacking. Both Sorvin and Praygat are killed by the creatures. But there's no time to grieve – the Doctor and Christina have to get back to the bus, before the Stingray swarm reaches it. It's not the Crystal the Doctor actually needs. It's the antigravity clamps that hold it in place. With the gold from the Cup of Athelstan as a final, vital ingredient, the bus is flying. They get through the wormhole, and Malcolm closes it before the swarm arrives. Three of the creatures do get through, and UNIT manages to shoot them down.

The police arrive to arrest Christine – but, with a bit of help from the Doctor, she escapes. In a flying bus!

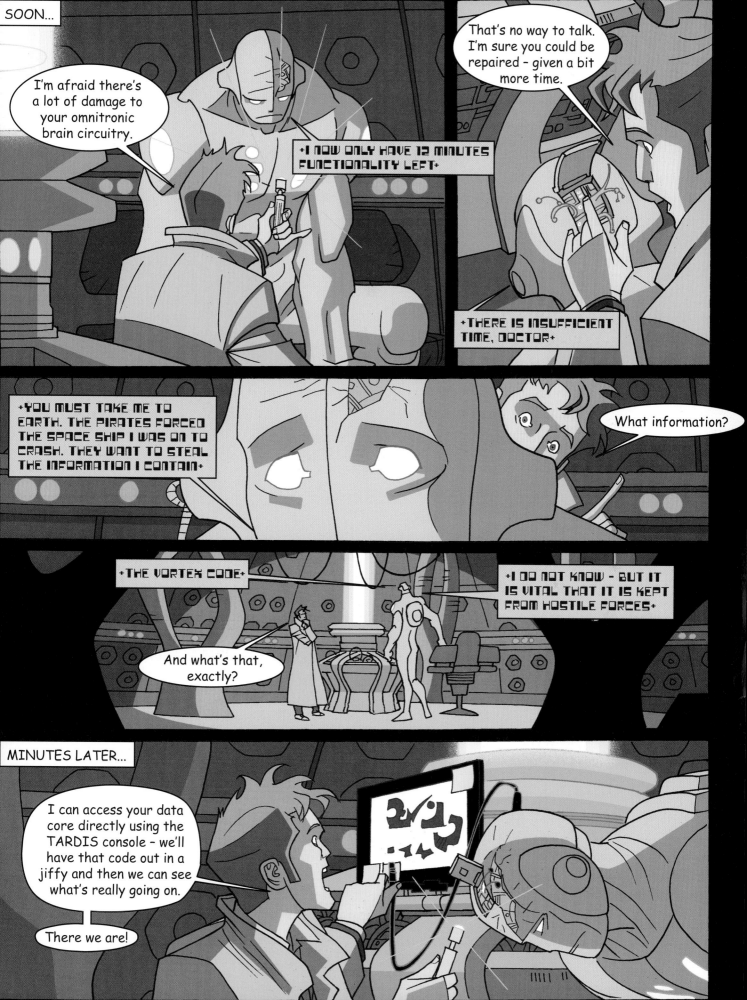

5 fantastic adventures

Moon-landing

Martha first met the Doctor when the Judoon took her hospital and dropped it on the moon. She bravely helped him track down an escaped alien and the Doctor offered her a trip in the TARDIS to say thank you.

History Lessons

Martha ended up working in an English boys' school in 1913 while the Doctor hid from the Family of Blood. Only Martha knew the Doctor's secrets, and that he was hiding his Time Lord self inside an old fob watch.

The Doctor and... Martha

Martha Jones was training to be a doctor when she met the Time Lord. She fell in love with the Doctor immediately — but he didn't realise! Eventually, she decided to stay on Earth, but they're still great friends and she always knows how to get in touch with him if she (or the planet) needs him.

Fast Facts

- Martha's cousin Adeola looked very like her, and was killed when Cybermen invaded Torchwood Tower.

- Her mum, dad and sister all ended up working as servants of the Master for a year.

- Martha is now working for UNIT.

Saving the World

When the Master and the Toclafane invaded Earth, it was up to Martha to spend a year travelling the world telling everyone she met about the Doctor and that he could save them.

Back on Earth

After she stopped travelling with the Doctor in the TARDIS, the first time she contacted him was to help with a UNIT investigation. Martha was later cloned by the Sontarans...

Journey's End

While she was working in New York, the Daleks invaded Earth. Martha risked her life by using an adapted Sontaran teleport to save herself — and used the Osterhagen Key as a threat to destroy the planet.

Time And Relative Dimension In Space

The TARDIS is capable of travelling anywhere in time and space by making use of the power of the Time Vortex. TARDIS is an acronym for Time And Relative Dimension In Space and the first thing that any visitor remarks upon is that it is bigger on the inside than the outside.

'It's the TARDIS. My TARDIS. Best ship in the Universe.' – The Doctor

Key to the door

The door of the TARDIS appears to be made out of wood and the means of opening it looks like an ordinary Yale key. However, the key to the TARDIS is anything but ordinary, for it opens up a whole universe of possibilities. The keys the Doctor gives to his companions heat up and glow when the TARDIS is about to materialise.

One of a Kind

Being the last of its kind, just like its owner, the TARDIS is like no other ship in the Universe. Among its unique properties it is capable of hacking into flight computers, tracking objects across time and space, towing other ships - and even planets! - to safety, converting a Time Lord into a human being, reading data-chip technology, defying the gravitational pull of a black hole, and even performing atmospheric excitations, in order to make it snow!

Coral buttress

The TARDIS is an organic craft and was grown on Gallifrey by the Time Lords. It is linked to the Doctor and his companions via a telepathic field, enabling it to translate languages automatically inside their heads. This works for written language as well.

Chameleon circuit

A fully functioning TARDIS is able to change its appearance to help it blend in with its background, wherever it lands. The chameleon circuit in the Doctor's TARDIS is faulty, leaving his ship stuck in the form of a 1950s Police Public Call Box. However, the TARDIS also generates a perception filter which helps reinforce the idea to anyone who may be looking at it, that it has every right to be there.

Best before

The Doctor's ship is actually an obsolete Type 40 TARDIS, also known as a TT Capsule. He unofficially 'borrowed' the ship when he left his home planet of Gallifrey centuries ago.

Saved by the bell

The TARDIS' internal alarm system is the Cloister Bell, which rings when the ship is in imminent danger.

Time rotor

The central column that rises from the console is the Time Rotor. When the TARDIS is in flight, the column moves up and down like a slowly-moving piston.

In case of emergency

Oxygen masks are fitted into the roof of the Console Room, along with the Chameleon Arch. The Doctor also carries a medical kit on-board. The TARDIS is encoded with the protocol 'Emergency Program One', which will return the Doctor's companion to Earth when activated.

Bigger on the inside...

The TARDIS is 'dimensionally transcendental', meaning that its exterior and interior exist in separate dimensions. This explains how the TARDIS can be bigger on the inside than the outside.

Precisely how big the TARDIS is on the inside is unknown, but it definitely contains an attic, a wardrobe, an art gallery, a greenhouse and a secondary control room.

Console

The TARDIS was designed to be piloted by six Time Lords. The hexagonal console has basic flight controls — including a dimensional stabiliser, vector tracker, and the vortex loop — a gravitic anomalyser, helmic regulator, a scanner and an extrapolator. There is also a hand-brake, a trim phone, a glass paperweight, a bell, a bicycle pump, and a mallet — for those times when the TARDIS needs a little 'percussive maintenance' — in other words, a good thump.

The Heart of the TARDIS

The temporal radiation — or time energy — that powers the TARDIS is stored at its heart, trapped beneath the central console. At times of extreme jeopardy, the TARDIS console has split apart, allowing the ship's soul to communicate directly with those on board. The TARDIS briefly died when it fell through the Void to the parallel Earth. The Doctor used his own internal energies — sacrificing a decade of his own life — to charge a crystal power source that then resuscitated the ship.

Storeroom

The TARDIS also has a storeroom directly underneath the Console Room, accessed via a panel in the floor. Amongst other things, it contains a trunk filled with clutter that all begins with the letter C, including a Cyberman chest plate, the Carrionites' crystal ball and a book by Agatha Christie.

29

Nightmare Creatures

Some monsters are almost too scary for words! The Doctor has met them all — and, luckily for those around them, he usually knows how to stop them.

The Scarecrows

The Family of Blood used molecular fringe animation to make an army of silent, scary and very sinister Scarecrow soldiers.

WHAT THE STRAW SERVANTS DID
· Found human bodies for the Family to use.
· Helped find the Doctor.
· Located the TARDIS.

The Weeping Angels

In one word — terrifying! The first time you see them, the Weeping Angels appear to be just stone statues. But take your eyes off them, or blink, and these creatures can move. And they need YOU so they can survive. Their touch will throw you back into the past...

ANGEL ADVICE!
· Stay calm.
· Don't let it touch you!
· Whatever you do, don't blink!

The Beast

Trapped in a pit on an inhospitable planet near a black hole, the horrific Beast used Toby Zed and the Ood to escape his prison.

IS THE BEAST NEAR?
· Have you got ancient writing on your hands and face?
· Are your eyes red?
· Are your Ood servants acting strangely?
· If the answer to each of these questions is YES then it might be too late...

Reapers

Huge, winged horrors, you know something has gone wrong when the Reapers appear. Living off wounds in time, the Reapers attack everything in sight in an attempt to sterilise the wound.

HOW TO AVOID
- Don't interfere with, or change, time.
- Don't let the TARDIS take you to a time that upsets you.
- Don't shake hands with a younger version of yourself.

Vashta Nerada

The Vashta Nerada live in shadows and are found in the dark. Piranhas of the air, the Vashta Nerada can strip human flesh in seconds.

WHO TURNED OUT THE LIGHTS?
- People are scared of the dark because of these creatures.
- Don't let their shadow touch yours.
- Vashta Nerada are cruel — so it's best to avoid them!

Midnight Monster

We don't know much about this nightmare creature, other than it started tapping on the side of a Crusader 50 shuttle bus and then took over a woman called Sky Silvestry.

WHAT IT DOES...
- Starts to repeat what you are saying.
- Then it says things at the same time.
- Finally, it speaks first and you follow.

What scares you about these creatures?
- Is it because some of them are silent or invisible?
- Or because they have fangs or fiery breath?
- Or is it because there's one behind you now? RUN!

Race against Time

28

27 Shakespeare banishes the Carrionites — go on 4

Transported to the Moon by the Judoon — miss a go

25

Stop the Empress of the Racnoss — roll again

Rose is trapped on Parallel Earth — miss 2 goes

22

The Battle of Canary Wharf — miss a go

Taken to Torchwood Tower — go on 2

19

Fear her! Flee from the Scribble Monster — go back 2

Escape the Abzorbaloff — go on 2

16

Best the Beast — roll again

Attacked by the Ood on the Impossible Planet — miss a go

13

Gridlock! Stuck in the worst traffic jam ever! — miss a go

Daleks invade Manhattan — go back 2

31

The Dalek Sec Hybrid is defeated — go on 5

Run from the Lazarus Creature — go back 5

34

Burn with me. The Sun-Possessed are after you — go back 4

You will need:
2-4 playing pieces
1 dice

INSTRUCTIONS
• Roll the dice to see who starts. The person who rolls the highest number goes first. (If two people both get the same highest number, they should roll again.)
• Players take it in turns to roll the dice and move their playing pieces forwards by the number of squares shown on the dice. They then follow any instructions on the square they land on.
• The first person to reach the final square is the winner.

4

Chased by Cat Nurses on New Earth — go back 2

Defeat the Sycorax with a tangerine — go on 2

Trapped in Torchwood House by a Werewolf — miss a go

School Reunion — K-9 saves the day! — roll again

7

Tick-tock! Tick-tock! Clockwork robots attack — go back 4

The Cybermen rise. Delete! Delete! — go back to the START

10

Defeat the Cyber-Controller — go on 5

Trap the Wire on a vintage videotape — go on 1

1 START

Photocopy or trace the playing pieces and stick them onto card. Alternatively you can use buttons or counters.

POLICE

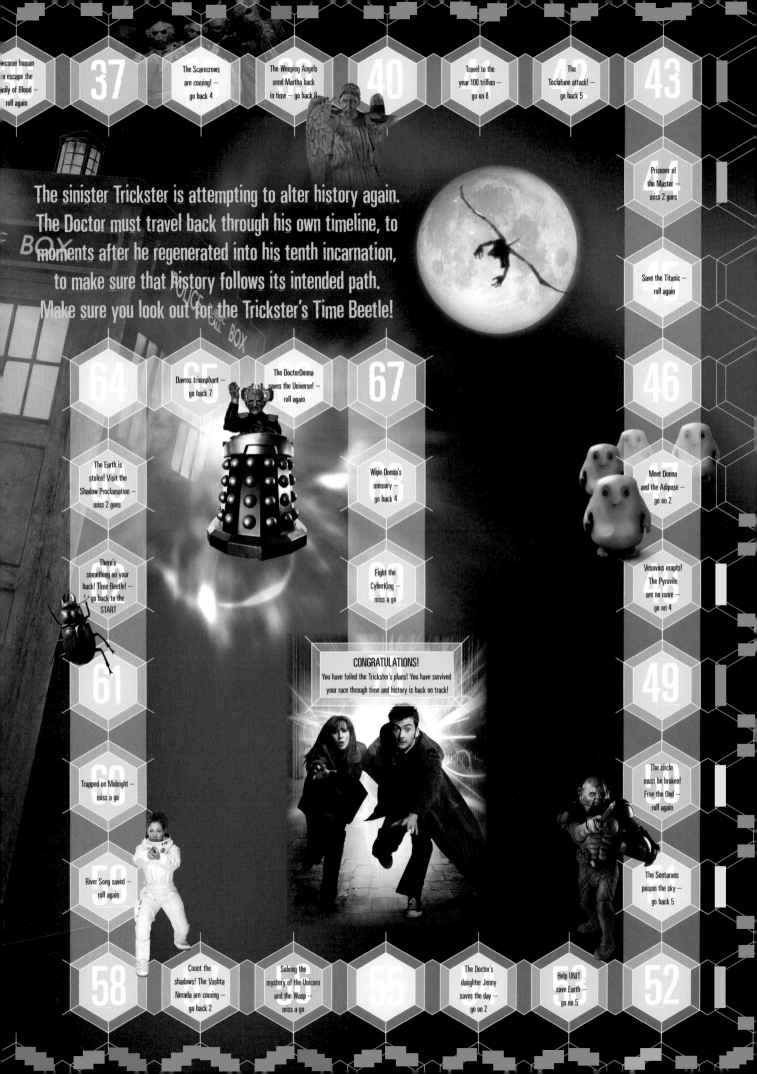

37

Become human to escape the family of Blood — roll again

The Scarecrows are coming! — go back 4

The Weeping Angels send Martha back in time — go back 8

40

Travel to the year 100 trillion — go on 8

The Toclafane attack! — go back 5

43

Prisoner of the Master — miss 2 goes

Save the Titanic — roll again

46

The sinister Trickster is attempting to alter history again. The Doctor must travel back through his own timeline, to moments after he regenerated into his tenth incarnation, to make sure that history follows its intended path. Make sure you look out for the Trickster's Time Beetle!

64

Davros triumphant — go back 7

The DoctorDonna saves the Universe! — roll again

67

Meet Donna and the Adipose — go on 2

The Earth is stolen! Visit the Shadow Proclamation — miss 2 goes

Wipe Donna's memory — go back 4

Vesuvius erupts! The Pyrovile are no more — go on 4

There's something on your back! Time Beetle! — go back to the START

Fight the CyberKing — miss a go

49

61

Trapped on Midnight — miss a go

CONGRATULATIONS!
You have foiled the Trickster's plans! You have survived your race through time and history is back on track!

The circle must be broken! Free the Ood — roll again

River Song saved — roll again

The Sontarans poison the sky — go back 5

58

Count the shadows! The Vashta Nerada are coming — go back 2

Solving the mystery of the Unicorn and the Wasp — miss a go

55

The Doctor's daughter Jenny saves the day — go on 2

Help UNIT save Earth — go on 5

52

Which Alien Are You?

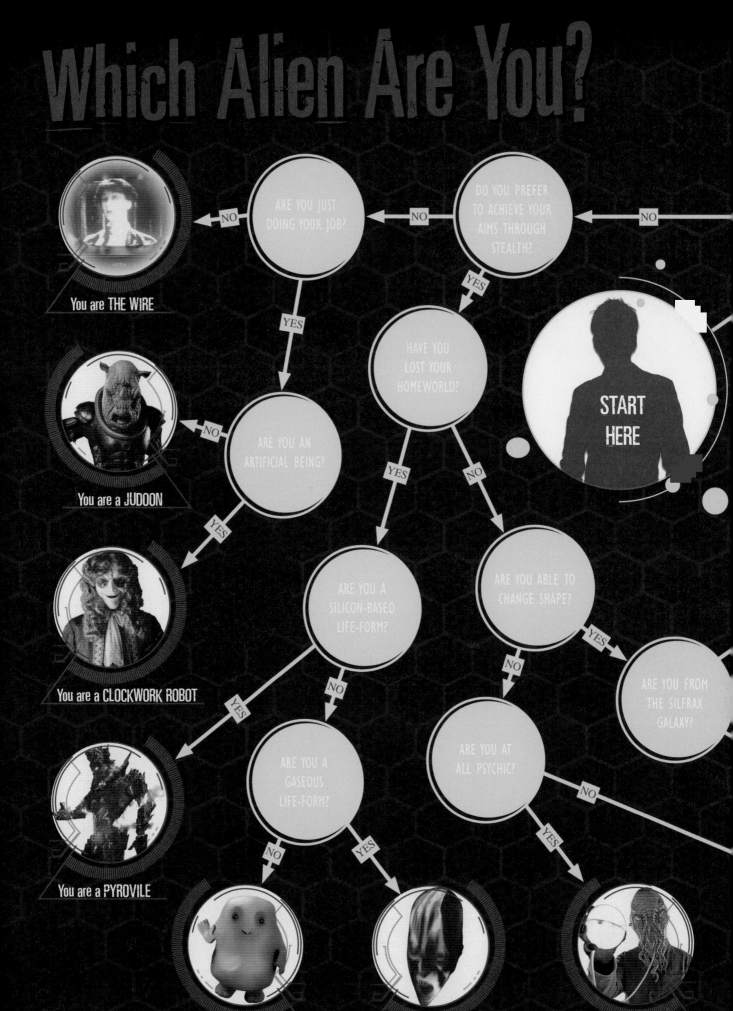

START HERE

DO YOU PREFER TO ACHIEVE YOUR AIMS THROUGH STEALTH? — NO →

— YES ↓

ARE YOU JUST DOING YOUR JOB? — NO → You are THE WIRE

— YES ↓

HAVE YOU LOST YOUR HOMEWORLD?

ARE YOU AN ARTIFICIAL BEING? — NO → You are a JUDOON

— YES ↓ You are a CLOCKWORK ROBOT

ARE YOU A SILICON-BASED LIFE-FORM? — YES → You are a PYROVILE

— NO ↓

ARE YOU ABLE TO CHANGE SHAPE? — YES → ARE YOU FROM THE SILFRAX GALAXY?

— NO ↓

ARE YOU A GASEOUS LIFE-FORM? — NO → You are AN ADIPOSE

— YES → You are the GELTH

ARE YOU AT ALL PSYCHIC? — YES → You are an OOD

— NO →

It's a dog-eat-dog Universe out there, and it takes a lot to survive. But do you have what it takes? Follow the flowchart to find out which alien you are.

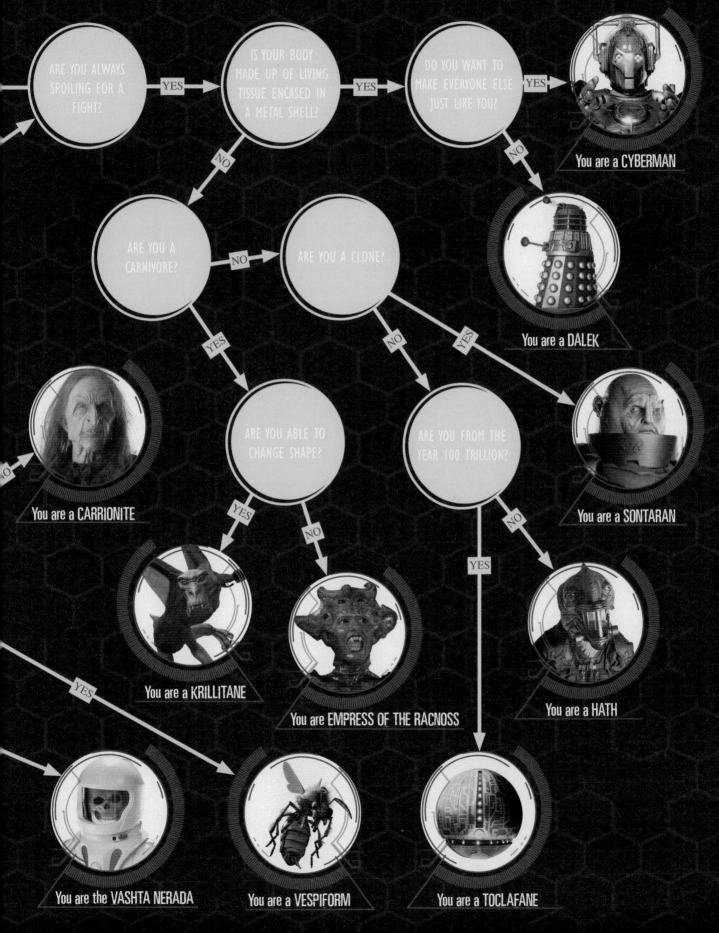

ARE YOU ALWAYS SPOILING FOR A FIGHT? — YES → IS YOUR BODY MADE UP OF LIVING TISSUE ENCASED IN A METAL SHELL? — YES → DO YOU WANT TO MAKE EVERYONE ELSE JUST LIKE YOU? — YES → You are a CYBERMAN

DO YOU WANT TO MAKE EVERYONE ELSE JUST LIKE YOU? — NO → You are a DALEK

IS YOUR BODY MADE UP OF LIVING TISSUE ENCASED IN A METAL SHELL? — NO → ARE YOU A CARNIVORE?

ARE YOU A CARNIVORE? — NO → ARE YOU A CLONE?

ARE YOU A CARNIVORE? — YES → ARE YOU ABLE TO CHANGE SHAPE?

ARE YOU A CLONE? — YES → You are a SONTARAN

ARE YOU A CLONE? — NO → ARE YOU FROM THE YEAR 100 TRILLION?

You are a CARRIONITE

ARE YOU ABLE TO CHANGE SHAPE? — YES → You are a KRILLITANE

ARE YOU ABLE TO CHANGE SHAPE? — NO → You are EMPRESS OF THE RACNOSS

ARE YOU FROM THE YEAR 100 TRILLION? — NO → You are a HATH

ARE YOU FROM THE YEAR 100 TRILLION? — YES → You are a TOCLAFANE

You are the VASHTA NERADA

You are a VESPIFORM

You are a TOCLAFANE

Cybermenace!

How much do you know about the Cybermen, their allies and their enemies? How many of the words listed below can you find inside the wordsearch? Are you ready for the Ultimate Upgrade or will you be deleted?

```
O P B I H E O I N H I B I T O R F U
V C Q R B I D K R L R O N K J O I H
Y T H E D A R G P U B D F L W P J E
S O O F A I H J R K M E L O S T G O P F
J I R O M U P O A E I C Y S K I W H Y I
A J C Y O K X R D S G F E T A E H N R D
F C T H L H V S C H O P A R A L L E L T Z P
L K E W H A O P I T T S K I M T P I U H A H
I S C O M E H A T V R R O Y P R B B M E R O
P O L O N T C Y B E R M A N I K E Y I Y C A R E
O N L D C E Y M U S Y W P E C G I O C C A E D
C L I A R H B S S F J T I J S Y K P A D P D
K A U P N S U Y D H A R T I G A N U I N C A
L K E H T O S M I R S U V F W B E H T A R E
T E A R I X I J A G E O F S T E E L E R B L
M S W K M E N T R N Z I L E I J A T I Y V R
E F K C A J D W O O P E G H S I R K S W I E
Y C A T D Y U R K M G O N I E C P O R H D B
O C Y B E R S H A D E C I P C R O E G A H Y
Z S D E V H T S J M Y H K N S H D H K R L C
T L B R M A R S Y E T F R I T S E U R F S I
I N H S E K I H F R A D E L E T E X Y O D E
E F T J M E R C Y I W B O S D W O F N I
S U L S W G T H S Y K D J I O E
A G E N A P R C Y G F S M
O K V S O J T V Y C H
F R O S I T A M
I U R L G S
```

Words to find:

CYBERMAN	DELETE	PARALLEL	JACKSON LAKE
CYBERLEADER	JOHN LUMIC	EARTH	ROSITA
CYBERSHADE	CYBUS INDUSTRIES	TORCHWOOD	MERCY
CYBERKING	EARPOD	AGE OF STEEL	HARTIGAN
HUMAN POINT TWO	EMOTIONAL	CANARY WHARF	
UPGRADE	INHIBITOR	INFO-STAMP	

Spellbreaker!

The Carrionites have invaded Elizabethan England using their spell-casting science to manipulate matter through the power of words. Can you break the Carrionite code and work out how to send them back to the Deep Darkness?

For Sooth, Nonny Nonny, Sooth I am But A Worm.

_ _ _ _ _ _ _ _

I am Unworthy, My Lords, A Peasant, My Lords.

_ _ _ _ _ _ _

I am Foolish, My Lords, But Would A Fool Trouble My Lords?

_ _ _ _ _ _ _ _ _

I am, Nonny, No Worm, My Lords!

_ _ _ _ _

Lily - livered —Hey —Foolish? No!

_ _ _ _

I am, Nonny, I am No, No Worm, My Lords.

_ _ _ _

Worm — Hey — Would Foolish Hey Dance For Hey?

_ _ _ _

Sing, My Lords, Now For — Hey — Foolish Sirrah-A.

_ _ _ _ _ _

Substitute the words of Love's Labour's Won with the correct letters from the box below to find out how to defeat the treacherous Lilith, Mother Bloodtide and Mother Doomfinger.

Word	Letter	Word	Letter	Word	Letter
A	S	I am	A	Sing	V
But	M	Lily-livered	P	Sirrah	D
Dance	F	My Lords	E	Sooth	I
Fool	T	No	T	Trouble	S
Foolish	R	Nonny	L	Unworthy	K
For	W	Now	N	Worm	H
Hey	O	Peasant	P	Would	U

Ultimate Alien Fighting Championship

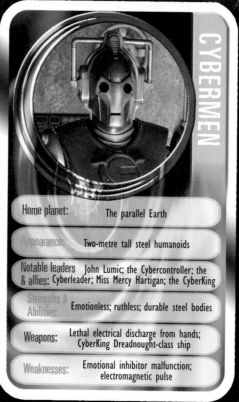

CYBERMEN

Home planet:	The parallel Earth
Appearance:	Two-metre tall steel humanoids
Notable leaders & allies:	John Lumic; the Cybercontroller; the Cyberleader; Miss Mercy Hartigan; the CyberKing
Strengths & Abilities:	Emotionless; ruthless; durable steel bodies
Weapons:	Lethal electrical discharge from hands; CyberKing Dreadnought-class ship
Weaknesses:	Emotional inhibitor malfunction; electromagnetic pulse

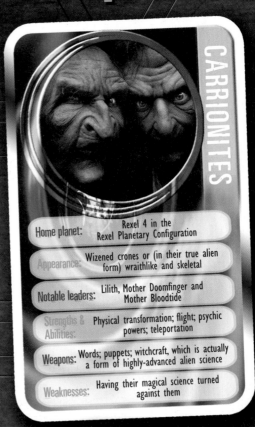

CARRIONITES

Home planet:	Rexel 4 in the Rexel Planetary Configuration
Appearance:	Wizened crones or (in their true alien form) wraithlike and skeletal
Notable leaders:	Lilith, Mother Doomfinger and Mother Bloodtide
Strengths & Abilities:	Physical transformation; flight; psychic powers; teleportation
Weapons:	Words; puppets; witchcraft, which is actually a form of highly-advanced alien science
Weaknesses:	Having their magical science turned against them

PYROVILES

Home planet:	Pyrovillia
Appearance:	Eight-metre tall giants of living rock and magma
Notable allies:	The High Priestess of the Sibylline Sisterhood; the Sibylline Sisterhood of Pompeii; Lucius Petrus Dextrus; the Cult of Vulcan
Strengths & Abilities:	Psychic contact and manipulation
Weapons:	Exhaled flame
Weaknesses:	Water

DALEKS

Home planet:	Skaro
Appearance:	One-eyed, tentacled mutants secured within tank-like life-support machines
Notable leaders:	Davros, The Emperor Dalek; the Cult of Skaro; the Supreme Dalek;
Strengths & abilities:	Emotionless; ruthless; flight; force-field protection; polycarbide Dalekanium armoured shell; incredibly fast decryption and decoding; genetic manipulation
Weapons:	Projected energy weapon; sucker arm; Reality Bomb
Weaknesses:	Eyestalk susceptible to concentrated firepower; arrogance; lack of imagination

The Doctor has encountered hordes of ruthless and powerful extraterrestrials during his centuries–long life, but how would these alien armies fare against each other? We present here for you some of the most terrible alien armies from across the vast reaches of space and time. You decide which would win the Ultimate Alien Fighting Championship!

TOCLAFANE

Home planet:	Utopia
Appearance:	Wizened human heads, encased within technologically advanced metal spheres
Notable leaders:	The Master
Strengths & Abilities:	Flight; species-wide telepathic link
Weapons:	Blades; laser weapons; 200,000 war rockets equipped with black hole converters
Weaknesses:	Child-like; insane; total reliance on the Paradox Machine to exist in our timeline

JUDOON

Home planet:	Unknown
Appearance:	Helmeted and armoured, bipedal, interstellar policemen
Notable leaders & allies:	Judoon Captain; the Shadow Proclamation; the Shadow Architect
Strengths & Abilities:	Fleet of spaceships; honourable; efficient
Weapons:	H_2O scoop plasma coil technology
Weaknesses:	A tendency to be overly-methodical; slow-witted

KRILLITANES

Home planet:	Unknown
Appearance:	Varies, but currently winged with sharp teeth and claws
Notable leaders:	Brother Lassar; the Chosen Few
Strengths & Abilities:	Morphic transformation; mild telepathy; flight
Weapons:	Chip-fed, super-intelligent children; sharp teeth; claws; a healthy carnivorous appetite
Weaknesses:	Loud noises; Krillitane Oil

SONTARANS

Home planet:	Sontar
Appearance:	Near-identical clone-bred armoured warriors, 1.5 metres tall, with hairless heads
Notable leaders & allies:	General Staal; Commander Skorr; Lieutenant Skree; human child prodigy Luke Rattigan
Strengths & Abilities:	Expert military training; fearless of death; vast numbers; teleportation
Weapons:	Atmospheric Omission System (a.k.a ATMOS); blasters; human clone spies
Weaknesses:	A blow to the probic vent at the back of the neck will stun, and sometimes kill, a Sontaran

SYCORAX

Home planet:	Sycorax
Appearance:	Tall, skinless, red-eyed warriors, who favour skull helmets and blood-red robes, adorned with trophies of past conquests
Notable leaders:	Sycorax leader
Strengths & Abilities:	Marital artistry; chemical and biological manipulation; interstellar flight; teleportation
Weapons:	Blood control; broadsword; staff; electrified whip
Weaknesses:	Show of brute strength; reluctance to accept defeat; tangerines

And the winners of the Ultimate Alien Fighting Championship are the   !

Oh, hello! This isn't your cave, is it? Cause if it is, I'm really sorry about any smoke damage, only...
Only you crashed. Like us. I mean, we crashed too.
I'm sorry to hear that. Is it just the two of you or...?
Just us. We got to an escape pod, but I fear the rest of my crew weren't so fortunate.
If anyone else did survive, they'd have been lucky to escape the local predators.
That's Earth during the Cretaceous period for you. Lots of big, hungry dinosaurs, and not enough food to go round.
They did seem pleased to see us. I'm Flish, by the way, Science Officer, and this is my Commander, Amyt.
I'm the Doctor. Pleased to meet you, Flish. Now, first things first, we need to find out what brought both our ships down.
We hit a gravity spike, resonating from this planet. It ripped our ship out of hyperspace as we passed through the system.
Doctor, your ship. Is it still functioning? Can it get us out of here?
Until we find the cause of that spike, she isn't going **anywhere**. I think it's time we had a look around, don't you?
Do you see anything?
A lot of not very much. Where did you say your escape pod came down?
Due south of here, not far from the caves where we met you. She took some damage on impact. There's not much left of her.

Enough to get my bearings. With the positions of your pod and the TARDIS, all I need is a third coordinate to **triangulate** the epicentre of the... Whoah there!

What is it, Doctor?

I think I might have found our gravity spike. This way.

Are you sure?

If I had a hat, I'd bet my hat on it. If I was a betting man... Massive bursts of graviton energy, a couple of miles or so north by north west.

ack

ack

ack

SKRAWRRRR!

The signal is off the scale. We must be getting close.

Doctor, watch out!

Ooof! I'd tell you you've got lovely teeth, but I don't suppose flattery will get me anywhere.

THE END

Donna's adventures

The Runaway Bride

On her wedding day, Donna was pulled into the TARDIS because her husband-to-be had fed her strange alien particles. Missing her wedding, she found herself travelling in time and fighting the Racnoss — but she decided travelling in the TARDIS was not for her.

Change of heart

Almost as soon as Donna said goodbye to the Doctor, she changed her mind. The only way she could think of tracking him down was by looking at strange things that were happening on Earth. A year later she ran into him while she was investigating Adipose Industries.

The Doctor and... Donna

Bold, brave and bright, super temp Donna Noble was unlike any other friend the Doctor ever met. She turned down his offer to travel with him at first... and then spent a year looking for him.

- Donna's fiancé was working for the Empress of the Racnoss — and didn't really want to marry her.

- She lived in Chiswick with her mum and her granddad.

- If Donna remembers any of her adventures with the Doctor, she will die.

History lesson

Jumping at a second chance to roam all of time and space, Donna's first trip in the TARDIS took her to Pompeii in 79 AD. Much to the annoyance of the Doctor, she immediately set about warning the people of Pompeii about the eruption of Mount Vesuvius — but, after begging him, was able to persuade the Doctor to save an entire family.

Meeting the Ood

When visiting the Ood-Sphere, Donna was appalled by the cruelty to the Ood and was reduced to tears when the Doctor shared their song with her. She helped the Doctor uncover the secret of Ood Operations — that the Ood had a second brain cut out and have a translator ball put in its place to create ready-to-sell servants.

Return to Earth

Donna returned home when the Doctor's old friend Martha needed his help. Concerned about her mum and granddad she popped back to visit them but decided not to tell her mum that she was travelling with the Doctor. She later found herself aboard the Sontaran ship, and was able to help defeat the Sontarans.

Murder Mystery

Donna couldn't believe she was face to face with Agatha Christie when they arrived in England in the 1920s. She ended up looking for clues to a series of murders with her — and was attacked by a Vespiform while she was doing so!

The Seven-day War

Donna helped solve the secret of the planet Messaline when she, the Doctor and Martha ended up on the barren planet. She discovered plaques with numbers that indicated that the war between the Hath and the humans had lasted only a week and not hundreds of years.

Saved

While exploring a planet called the Library in the 51st century, Donna became saved on to the Library hard drive and suddenly found herself married with two children — although later discovered this was just part of the strange virtual world.

Holiday Time

When the Doctor couldn't convince Donna to explore a holiday planet called Midnight with him, Donna decided to relax by a swimming pool in the main complex — but was later disturbed to find out about the dangers he'd encountered there

A World Without the Doctor

Wandering into a fortune teller's room on the Chino-planet of Shan Shen, poor Donna was attacked by a Time Beetle — and suddenly found herself in a parallel Earth without the Doctor.

It was there that she met someone the Doctor used to know very well: Rose Tyler.

With Rose's help, Donna was able to go back in time by using a near dead TARDIS and set time on its correct path again.

Journey's End

When the Daleks stole Earth, Donna found herself fighting alongside Rose, Jack, Sarah Jane, Martha, Jackie and Mickey to save the entire universe.

Dalek Caan had been tampering with the timelines to ensure that Donna and the Doctor met. He helped to bring Donna to the right place in time and space so that she could rid the universe of Daleks.

Becoming half-Time Lord when she touched the Doctor's spare hand she was able to save the universe, but being part-alien nearly killed her.

So, sadly, the Doctor has to remove all Donna's memories of her time with him in order to save her and takes her back to Earth. Donna Noble was one of the most important people in the universe — and she had no idea.

The Epic Tenth Doctor Quiz

How well do you know the Tenth Doctor? Answer the questions to find out!

1 What colours are the Tenth Doctor's two favourite suits?

(a)   Brown and red

(b)   Brown and blue

(c)   Green and brown

2 Which of the following companions hasn't travelled with the Tenth Doctor in the TARDIS?

(a)   Rose Tyler

(b)   Captain Jack

(c)   Adam Mitchell

3 Who did the Doctor originally think Jackson Lake was?

(a)   A half-converted Cyberman

(b)   An old friend

(c)   The next or future version of himself

4 What was the name of the episode that the Tenth Doctor made his first appearance in?

(a)   The Christmas Invasion

(b)   Parting of the Ways

(c)   The Next Doctor

5 What planet did the Tenth Doctor take Rose to after they'd defeated the Sycorax?

(a)   Krop Tor

(b)   Utopia

(c)   New Earth

6 What does 'Allons-y!' mean?

(a)   'I'm the last of the Time Lords!'

(b)   'It travels through time!'

(c)   'Let's go!'

7 Where did the Doctor and Donna first meet?

(a)   In the TARDIS

(b)   At her wedding

(c)   On the moon

8 What relation did the Doctor meet on the planet Messaline?

(a)   His father

(b)   His daughter

(c)   His granddaughter

9 What helped the Doctor stabilise after he regenerated?

(a)   Some hot tea

(b)   A banana

(c)   The sonic screwdriver

10 Which of these people has the Tenth Doctor not met?

(a)   Agatha Christie

(b)   Queen Victoria

(c)   Charles Dickens

11 What did the Master do to the Doctor on board the Valiant?

(a)   Aged him

(b)   Made him cook

(c)   Made him fly the TARDIS

12 Who was *The Girl in the Fireplace*?

(a)   Martha Jones

(b)   Madame de Pompadour

(c)   Sarah Jane Smith

BAD BAD WOLF WOLF

13 What does Queen Victoria knight the Doctor as?

(a)   Sir John Smith

(b)   Sir Doctor Who

(c)   Sir Doctor of TARDIS

14 Which person on the Titanic wanted to travel with the Doctor?

(a)   Astrid Peth

(b)   Foon van Hoff

(c)   Bannakaffalatta

15 Who helped the Doctor return a bus back to Earth in Planet of the Dead?

(a)   Lady Christina de Souza

(b)   Lady Macbeth

(c)   Donna Noble

16 What number bus travelled through a wormhole in time and space?

(a)   The 200

(b)   The 271

(c)   The 268

17 Where did the Doctor last see Rose Tyler?

(a)   Bad Wolf Bay on a parallel Earth

(b)   The Dalek Crucible in deep space

(c)   At the Torchwood Institute

18 What happened when a Dalek shot at the Tenth Doctor in The Stolen Earth?

(a)   He dodged it and ran back to the TARDIS

(b)   It missed and hit Rose and Donna instead

(c)   It hit the Doctor causing him to start regenerating

19 What happened to the Doctor's spare hand?

(a)   It was left in a container in the TARDIS

(b)   A new Doctor grew out of the hand when Donna touched it

(c)   The Daleks exterminated it

20 How does Carmen warn the Doctor?

(a)   Tells him, 'Beware the falling brick.'

(b)   Says, 'He will knock four times.'

(c)   Warns him, 'Don't touch that button.'

Alien Armies

Daleks

Without doubt, the Daleks are the deadliest and most powerful army of all. Created by a genius scientist called Davros, these encased creatures will stop at nothing to destroy other races and conquer worlds.

Lead by: Davros (until the Daleks replaced him), the Dalek Emperor and the Supreme Dalek.

Special skills: flight, replaceable arms, lack of emotion, energy shield.

Listen out for: 'Exterminate!'

Ood

The Ood are gentle telepathic creatures, found on most planets in the Second Great and Bountiful Human Empire. However, the Ood are easily taken over by stronger minds. They became an army for the Beast.

Lead by: the Ood Brain on the Ood-Sphere, the Beast on Krop Tor.

Skills: telepathic communication, slightly psychic, translator balls can be used to kill.

Listen out for: 'We are the legion of the Beast!'

The Hath

The bubbling Hath are half-fish, half-human and came to the planet Messaline with a group of humans. War broke out between the Hath and the humans — and massive armies of Hath were created with Progenation Machines.

Lead by: Hath ranks are unknown.

Skills: determination, Progenation.

Listen out for: bubbling speech.

Judoon

Big, thick creatures — the Judoon will be your own private army, if you can afford them.

Lead by: the Judoon Captain. The Judoon have been known to work for the Shadow Proclamation.

Skills: ability to identify languages and species, strength, determination.

Listen out for: 'Justice is swift!' and 'Sco! Bo Tro! No! Flo! Jo! Ko! Fo! To! Do!'

Sontarans

Short and ugly aliens, the Sontarans are a race of clones. These creatures are bred for war by the million and have been fighting with the Rutans for thousands of years.

Lead by: a Sontaran General works alongside Commanders.

Skills: cloning, military minds.

Listen out for: 'Sontar-ha!'

Sycorax

Horrific warrior monsters, armies of bone-faced Sycorax travel long distances in massive stone spaceships to invade worlds by tricking them into surrendering.

Lead by: the Sycorax Leader.

Skills: blood control, sword fighting.

Listen out for: 'Sycorax rock!'

Cybermen

Created on a parallel Earth by John Lumic, the Cybermen were once like us. All that remains of their human self is a brain. A special emotional inhibitor stops the creatures from having any human feelings.

Lead by: John Lumic was upgraded to CyberController. Each army has a CyberLeader.

Special skills: strength, logic, one mind, almost immortal.

Listen out for: 'Delete!'

53

From Time Agent to Conman

The Doctor first ran into Captain Jack when he and Rose visited London at the height of the Blitz. Originally a Time Agent from the 51st century, Jack woke one morning to discover that two years of his memories had been stolen by his employers. On account of this, he set himself up as a freelance conman, travelling through time, salvaging alien space junk, and selling it back to the Time Agency.

The Empty Child

Basing himself in Westminster in 1941, Jack served as an American volunteer for the Royal Air Force, having assumed the identity of the real Captain Jack Harkness. On learning that he was actually the cause of the outbreak of Chula gas-mask zombies linked to the Albion Hospital, he helped the Doctor put things right. However, his ship was destroyed by a German bomb, and so he joined the Doctor and Rose on their travels.

Boom Town

Jack helped the Doctor thwart the plans of Blon Fel Fotch Pasameer-Day Slitheen who was on the run after her family nearly brought about World War Three. Having disguised herself as Margaret Blaine, the new Mayor of Cardiff, she moved to have a nuclear facility built at the heart of the city. She planned for the power station to go into meltdown, which would open Cardiff's space-time rift and destroy Earth, all so that she could escape back to her home planet of Raxacoricofallapatorius.

The Doctor and... Captain Jack

Debonair, dashing and charismatic, with a taste for 1940s fashions, Captain Jack Harkness has been many things in his long life, from a Time Agent, to a conman, to a Torchwood operative. Oh, and he cannot die.

The Parting of the Ways

Captain Jack's travels with the Doctor came to an end for a while, after he went down in a blaze of glory, fighting the Daleks in the year 200,100. However, he was brought back to life by Rose when she temporarily absorbed the power of the Time Vortex, making him immortal. The Doctor, unaware that Jack was alive, departed with Rose, leaving him trapped on the Game Station. Using his Vortex Manipulator, Jack travelled back to 19th century Earth and had to live through the entire 20th century while he waited for the Doctor's return.

Utopia

Captain Jack found the Doctor again when the TARDIS landed in Cardiff to refuel from the space-time rift. But the Doctor's ship tried to escape from what it recognised as something that shouldn't exist. It carried the Doctor and Martha 100 trillion years into the future, to the end of the Universe, taking Jack with it, clinging onto the outside!

The Year That Never Was

Jack was kept prisoner aboard the Valiant by the Master, during the Year That Never Was, being tortured and killed in an endless cycle of agonising death and resurrection. Freed when the Doctor overpowered the Master, Jack attacked and destroyed the Paradox Machine, allowing time to run backwards by a year and a day, undoing the damage caused by the Toclafane.

The Stolen Earth

More recently Captain Jack was one of the Children of Time who helped the Doctor stop a New Dalek Empire's plot to wipe out the whole of creation, after the aliens transported Earth inside the Medusa Cascade and invaded the planet once again. Jack threatened to use a Warp Star — an explosion waiting to happen — to destroy the Dalek's Crucible flagship. His ability to survive practically anything served him well once again.

And the future?

Who knows if, or more likely when, the Doctor's and Jack's paths will cross again, but it's quite possible that it has already happened. Captain Jack once told the Doctor and Martha that, back on the Boeshane Peninsula, the colony where he grew up, he was known as the Face of Boe. Could it be that Captain Jack is destined to become the prophet of the Doctor's future from the year 5,000,000,000?

Time Lord Technology

The Doctor and his companions have used all sorts of weird and wonderful devices in their battles against everything from the Cybermen to the Slitheen. Here we give you the lowdown on Time Lord Technology...

Sonic screwdriver

Able to open virtually any lock, the Doctor's sonic screwdriver uses sound waves to remotely exert physical force on an object. The one thing the Doctor wouldn't be without – other than his TARDIS – the sonic screwdriver seems to have an endless list of uses. It works as a radiation detector, remotely activates processes inside the TARDIS, is capable of detecting and sending signals, intercepts teleport beams, fuses metal, amplifies and augments sound waves, deactivates mechanical devices, can be used as a cutting tool and fixes broken Vortex Manipulators.

Did you know...? The sonic screwdriver cannot open objects locked with a deadlock seal, and some hair dryers can interfere with its signal. Oh, and it doesn't do wood.

The Doctor is not the only one with a sonic device. Sarah Jane has a sonic lipstick, the villainous Miss Foster had a sonic pen, and River Song had her own sonic screwdriver. Her improved version came with dampeners, red settings and even a neural relay data-chip, which the Doctor used to 'save' her consciousness after she 'died'.

Did you know...? The Doctor once had a laser spanner as well, until Emmeline Pankhurst, leader of the Women's Suffrage Movement, ran off with it.

Psychic paper

Psychic paper allows whoever is holding it to show other people whatever it is that they want them to see, whether it be an invitation to watch the end of the world or appropriate credentials with which to impress royalty. The Doctor keeps his psychic paper in a leather wallet.

Psychic paper also has the ability to display telepathic messages sent from anywhere in time and space. River Song uses it in this way to bring the Doctor to the Library in the 51st century, as does the Face of Boe, to summon him to New Earth in 5,000,000,023. If you're not careful, you can give away private details about yourself to other people through the psychic paper when you hand it over to them.

People who have had psychic training are not susceptible to the effects of psychic paper. The same goes for geniuses, such as William Shakespeare.

Ward 26
please come

Laser screwdriver

When Prime Minister Harry Saxon reveals himself to be the Master, he also revealed his laser screwdriver. He used it as a weapon, producing a directed laser beam capable of killing its target. Thanks to built-in hypersonic sound wave manipulation technology, developed by Lazarus Laboratories, it could also be used to age a person artificially. It had isomorphic controls, which meant that it could only be used by the Master.

Did you know...? The word LASER actually stands for Light Amplification by Stimulated Emission of Radiation.

Fob watch

A Time Lord's memories, and even his entire personality, can be stored within a watch. The Doctor had such a watch, engraved with Gallifreyan symbols, which was actually part of a Time Lord device known as a Chameleon Arch. The Chameleon Arch re-wrote a Time Lord's biology, then stored the individual's essence within the fob watch. The watch made use of a perception filter to stop the transformed Time Lord from noticing it, and inadvertently opening it.

Did you know...? The Doctor met a man in 1851 battling the Cybermen whom he at first thought was a future incarnation of himself. However, when this 'Next Doctor' took out his fob watch, it helped the true Doctor establish his identity as Jackson Lake, an ordinary human being caught up in extraordinary events.

Escape from the Library!

The Vashta Nerada — microscopic piranhas of the air — are after the Doctor as he tries to escape from The Library. Can you lead him from the Data Core to the Little Shop and safety?

DATA CORE

LITTLE SHOP

The name Vashta Nerada means 'the shadows that melt the flesh'. There are small numbers of these piranhas in the air on almost every planet where there is meat to be eaten, including Earth!

All Hail the CyberKing!

The CyberKing was the creation of a group of Cybus Cybermen who had escaped from the Void — where they had been trapped by the Doctor in 2007 — using stolen Dalek technology called a Dimension Vault. Falling back in time through the dimensions, they landed in Victorian London. They used the technology of the time to construct their CyberKing beneath the River Thames, exploiting child labour to stoke the massive steam engine needed to generate the necessary electricity to activate it.

The CyberKing was a Dreadnought Class Spaceship used in the frontline of a cyber invasion force. It was a bipedal walker that looked like a gigantic Cyberman and was armed with a whole arsenal of devastating weaponry, including a ballistic mortar and energy weapons, capable of laying waste to whole cities. The cyber-factory located inside its chest could then be used to upgrade the subjugated population and was capable of converting millions.

Like other cyber-devices, the CyberKing needed an organic brain to control it. The Cybermen found the perfect subject in Miss Mercy Hartigan, the bitter and vengeful matron of the Saint Joseph Workhouse. However, rather than being completely taken over by the cyber-software, Miss Hartigan's mind dominated the CyberKing's consciousness, allowing her to take control of not only the Dreadnought Class Ship but also the Cybermen themselves. Cyberman logic and strength combined with her very human fury and passion to create something new and utterly terrifying.

The Doctor broke the Cyber connection, leaving Miss Hartigan's mind open so that she truly understood what she had done and what she had become. This terrible knowledge killed her and overloaded the remaining Cybermen, destroying them as well.

Robbed of its controlling consciousness, the CyberKing started to break-up and looked like it was going to fall on London, causing untold damage, until the Doctor used the Dimension Vault to transfer the wreckage into the Time Vortex, where it would harmlessly disintegrate.

Could this really be the last the Doctor will see of the Cybermen?

Answers

Page 12

SECRETS OF THE DALEKS!

(crossword grid with answers including:) THE CRUCIBLE, DALEKANIUM, CAAN, SARO, TIMEWAR, TIME VORTEX, EMPIRE STATE BUILDING, STELLI, PIGSLAVES, HENRY VAN STATTEN, THE BATTLE OF CANARY WHARF, MUDI AGRAS, THE VAULT, RELS, VOIDSHIP, DAVROS, GENESIS ARK, REALITY BOMB, SUPREME DALEK

Page 36

CYBERMENACE!

(word search grid, words found: INHIBITOR, UPGRADE, PARALLEL, CYBERMAN, HARTIGAN, AGE OF STEEL, CYBERSHADE, DELETE, MERCY, ROSITA)

Page 13

DAVROS DETECTED!

Page 37

SPELLBOUND!

William Shakespeare must seal the portal at the hour of the woven words.

Page 50–51

THE EPIC TENTH DOCTOR QUIZ

Answers: 1 (b), 2 (c), 3 (c), 4 (b), 5 (c), 6 (c), 7 (a), 8 (b), 9 (a), 10 (c) Charles Dickens met the Ninth Doctor, 11 (a), 12 (b), 13 (c), 14 (a), 15 (a), 16 (a), 17 (a), 18 (c), 19 (b), 20 (b)

How did you score?

0-5 Have you had your mind wiped like Donna? Try again!

6-10 You might have to watch some old adventures again!

11-15 Good, but you could do better!

16-20 Well done — you certainly know the Tenth Doctor!

Page 58

ESCAPE FROM THE LIBRARY!

DATA CORE

LITTLE SHOP

DOCTOR · WHO

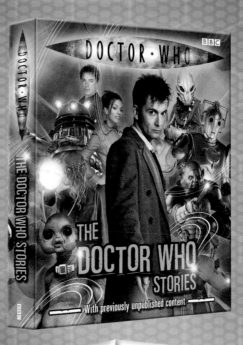